STARS HOLLOW COLORING BOOK

BROUGHT TO YOU BY PEGGY MARTINEZ & STARS HOLLOW MONTHLY

For those of us who wish we could visit Stars Hollow....

Oy! WITH the POODLES already

"Oh my God, I JUST GOT HIT by a deer!"

I'M A
Witty
CONVERSA-
TIONALIST

Lane

What she tackles She conquers

- Richard Gilmore

Michel, It's the first Snow fall of the Season It's very lucky. Make a Wish

HAVE I EVER BEEN *mistaken* FOR A *Patient person?*

— PARIS GELLER

LOGAN

HUNDRED YEARS

Without really

living

FOR A

Minute

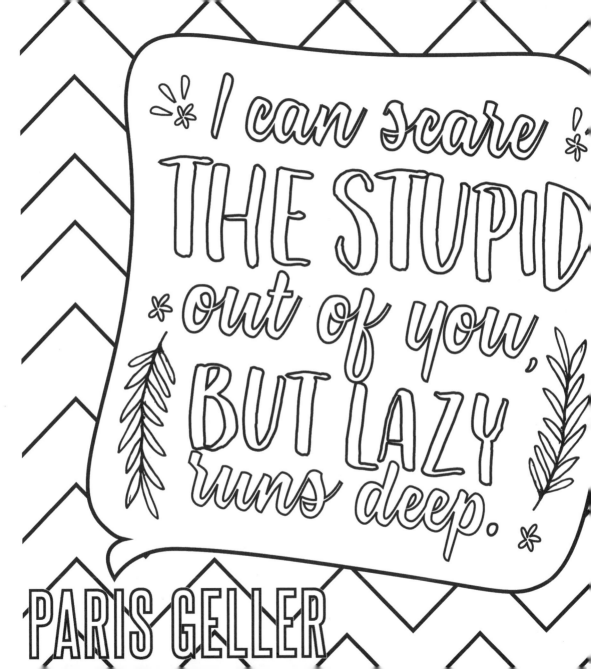

I can scare THE STUPID out of you, BUT LAZY runs deep.

PARIS GELLER

ARTWORK BY: DANIELLE STYLES

you can't watch WILLY WONKA without massive amounts of JUNK FOOD

-LORELAI

ARTWORK BY: DANIELLE STYLES

ARTWORK BY: NORA MURAD

I BELIEVE IN A FORMER LIFE I WAS COFFEE

Luke's